ENGLISH

Practice for
Key Stage 2
National tests

Ages 9–10

TEST
YOUR C[
ENGLISH

Reading Booklet pull-out

Test and Answer Booklet pull-out

Let's learn at home

ENGLISH

INTRODUCTION

What are the Key Stage 2 National Tests?

Every year in May, children in Year 6 (the final year of primary school or midway through middle school) take written National Tests. There are two English, three maths and two science tests. They are designed to show the levels of work your child is able to achieve in these three core subjects. The tests are carried out over one week. The papers are marked by external examiners. When returned to school, the results of the tests (commonly known as SATs) give parents and teachers an indication of each child's knowledge in relation to the standards set out in the National Curriculum (NC). They also provide a rough guide to how your child's school has performed in relation to other schools both locally and nationally.

What the test results mean

Along with assessments made by the class teacher, your child's National Test results will be sent to his or her secondary school and be used by the staff there to help them decide the most appropriate teaching groups for your child to be placed in.

About the English tests

The tests for English assess basic skills in reading, writing, spelling and handwriting, and consist of:
- a reading comprehension test
- a writing test, including a spelling and handwriting test
  (which may be taken as a separate test).

This mirrors the way the English National Curriculum is organized, with separate Programmes of Study for Reading and Writing. Each of the tests carries the same number of marks (ie 50 each). Marks gained in the separate tests are combined to determine each child's overall level of performance for English. This performance level is linked to the level indicators set out in the National Curriculum document for English.

How this book can help you to help your child

The practice papers in this book can help you prepare your child in the most realistic way possible for the end of Key Stage 2 National Tests in English. They will help to:
- familiarize your child with the format and layout of test papers
- familiarize your child with the type of questions in the tests
- indicate areas of strength or weakness
- approximate the level your child is working at in English.

Using this book

This book is made up of three booklets, each one separately stapled. Pull out the centre booklet first. This is the Test and Answer Booklet and has all the test papers for the Reading and Writing tests. There are separate instruction pages for each of the tests. We recommend that you read the instructions with your child, making sure they are understood before the test begins.

Next pull out the middle booklet, which is the Reading Booklet. This has fiction and information passages which have been selected for the Reading test. Your child will need to read and refer to the Reading Booklet during the Reading test. The remaining booklet has information on the tests, answers to the tests and the marks scheme, and will help you to set the test.

Taking the tests

Before you set the test

It is important that your child feels comfortable about sitting these practice papers. Explain that they should help him or her to become used to the kinds of activities in the actual tests.

At the start

The practice papers can be set in any order. The complete English test takes two and a quarter hours. Do each test on a separate day, at a time when your child is not tired or irritable, and in a quiet place with no distractions. Make sure you allow plenty of time for taking, marking and talking afterwards about the test. Be as positive as you can so that your child starts each test confidently. It is important he or she should not feel over-anxious or pressured. If your child shows any signs of distress, leave the test until a later date. Finally, read the instructions together carefully and ensure your child understands them.

During the test

How rigidly you observe the time-limits for these practice tests depends on how far you wish to replicate the actual test conditions. You may wish to insist on your child working entirely alone, asking no questions. Or you may prefer not to put your child under the pressure of keeping strictly to 'test conditions'. Working through practice papers is a perfectly valid test preparation activity. You could help your child increase speed by giving extra practice later. As with any skill, the more practice you have, the more efficient you become.

Once your child has started, don't fuss and keep looking over his or her shoulder. If your child finishes before the end of the test time, encourage him or her to go back and check answers. If your child does not finish before the time is up, stop the test, make a note of where your child is up to, then allow your child to finish the test, if he or she wishes. However, only that part of the test finished during the allowed time should be marked for the final test score.

For the Reading test, make sure your child has the Reading Booklet, the Test and Answer Booklet (referring to the Reading test section)
- spare paper for any notes
- pens or pencils
- a clock or watch to keep track of the time.

For the Writing test, your child will need the Test and Answer Booklet (referring to the Writing test, Spelling and Handwriting section)
- lined paper
- pens or pencils
- a clock or watch to keep track of the time.

Marking the answers

Pages 5–12 give suggested answers and marking guidelines for the practice tests. It is advisable to mark the papers with your child and discuss the answers as you go. That way, if he or she did not answer a question at all, you can try to find out why and discuss problems. Try not to be inflexible about 'right' or 'wrong' answers. The answers given are suggested guidelines only, and you need to make allowances for the different ways individuals express themselves.

● In the margin of each test paper, there is a mark box alongside each question part. Write the number of marks scored by your child for that part of the question in this box. If your child gets the question wrong, put '0' in the box. If your child does not attempt the question, put a '–' in the box. Do not leave any mark box empty.

● At the bottom of all the right-hand page margins is a 'total' box for the number of marks scored on that double (or single) page. Write each of these totals on to the 'marking grid' on the front cover of the test booklet and add them up.

● Transfer the final total mark to the correct text column of the first table on the inside back cover of this booklet.

What do National Curriculum Levels mean?

For children between the ages of 5 and 14 the National Curriculum is divided into eight levels of attainment. Children are expected to advance approximately one level for every two years they are at school. At the end of Key Stage 1, children are expected to be working at Level 2. By the end of Key Stage 2, it is expected they will be at Level 4. The table shows you at what level an average child should be working for each of the six years of primary school.

The KS2 National Test for English is geared towards Levels 3–5, with the expectation that most Year 6 children attempting it will be at Level 4. (It is worth noting that 63 per cent of children who sat the 1997 English test were judged to have achieved Level 4.) Very able children will be entered for an extension test that covers Level 6, which represents exceptional achievement for the age group.

Key Stage	Year	NC Level
1	1	1
1	2	2
2	3	2/3
2	4	3
2	5	3/4
2	6	4/5

This practice test is pitched for children working towards Level 4. Refer to the inside back cover to find your child's level. We recommend that both the Reading test and the Writing test are completed before you attempt to find your child's overall level.

Important note

In marking National Test papers, external markers use their professional judgement, based on years of experience. It is not to be expected that as a parent you will be able to bring the same experience and judgement to marking these practice papers. The marks you award and the level your child gains as a result of doing these practice papers may therefore differ from those that examiners or teachers at your child's school would give. Please remember too that the purpose of this book is to provide test practice for your child, as well as to highlight any areas of difficulty he or she may be having. We suggest that you use the information about your child's performance in these practice papers as a basis for discussion with your child's teacher, who will be able to offer advice and ideas for helping your child to improve in areas of need.

ANSWERS TO READING TEST
Don't Cut the Lawn! by Margaret Mahy (story)

Answers to pages 3–4

The answers to questions 1–8 are multiple choice. Your child's answer will be circled. Award **1 mark** for each correct choice.

1 by the sea
2 like a field
3 the lawnmower
4 a tussock of grass
5 the mother hare
6 the baby dragon
7 Snapping Jack was frightened of the mother dragon
8 went swimming

> **Parent's tip**
>
> **Questions 9–19** are open-ended. You need to decide whether your child's answer is correct or acceptable as correct. Be aware that there are different ways of wording an acceptable answer. Focus on the content of what your child has written.
> Do not penalize errors of spelling, grammar or punctuation in this part of the test. The quality of your child's response and understanding is being tested here, not spelling, handwriting, punctuation or grammar.

9 Focus of question: *deduction of character*
Award **1 mark** for answers along these lines:
- There were good hiding places in the tangly, tussocky lawn.
- The grass had been left to grow.
- It was quiet and safe in Mr Pomeroy's garden.
- No one had been in the garden to cut the lawn for a long time.

10 Focus of question: *deduction of character's motives*
Award **1 mark** for answers along these lines:
- He did not want to harm the baby creatures.
- He did not want to upset the mothers.
- Cutting the grass would disturb the nests.
- Cutting the grass would frighten the creatures.

11 Focus of question: *evaluation of character's feelings*
Award **1 mark** for short answers such as:
- It could blow out a tiny flame.
Award **2 marks** for more elaborate answers such as:
- The baby dragon could breathe out fire when it had just been born.
- The baby dragon was very pretty and could blow a tiny flame.

12 Focus of question: *finding evidence*
Award **1 mark** for each correct response (up to **3 marks**).
- She could burn the lawn.
- She could scorch off eyebrows.
- She could melt the lawnmower.

Answers to page 5

13 Focus of question: *deduction of character*
Award **2 marks** for a correct response along these lines:
- Snapping Jack was thinking that he did not want to disturb the mother dragon because she might melt him with her fiery breath.
- Snapping Jack was scared of what the mother dragon might do to him.

14 Focus of question: *insight into character and finding textual evidence*
Award **1 mark** for each answer that shows reference to the text (up to **3 marks**). These are some examples but there is a range of possible answers. You need to decide whether your child's answer is acceptable as correct.

dangerous
- The mother dragon might attack them by blowing out a big flame.

- The mother dragon would be upset if her baby got hurt.

beautiful

- She had jewelled eyes.
- She was green and golden.

frightening

- She said she could attack Mr Pomeroy.
- She was big and hissed.

brave

- She told Mr Pomeroy not to cut the lawn.
- She stared at them with jewelled eyes and hissed.

fierce

- She was big and hissed.
- She said she would blow out a very big flame.
- She would breathe fire hot enough to melt a lawnmower if her baby was hurt.
- She would hurt Mr Pomeroy and Snapping Jack if they mowed the grass near her baby.

protective

- She told Mr Pomeroy not to cut her baby dragon.
- She said she would hurt Mr Pomeroy and Snapping Jack if they mowed the grass near her baby.

15 Focus of question: *deduction/finding evidence*
Award **1 mark** for each of two answers along these lines (up to **2 marks**):

- The dragon was as green as the grass. ● The dragon was as golden as a tussock.
- The grass was a long, lank, tussocky tangle.
- The colour of the dragon was the same as the lawn.

16 Focus of question: *finding evidence*
Your child may choose to quote from the text, or to answer with his or her own opinion.
Award **1 mark** for an answer along these lines:

- 'There's more to a lawn then mere grass, you know!' (quoted from the story).
- That the environment is very important.
- That animals need to be protected.
- That we should respect animals' homes.

17 Focus of question: *inference*
Award **1 mark** for each correct response (up to **2 marks**).

- The dragon laid its shining head on Mr Pomeroy's knee.
- The dragon told Mr Pomeroy wonderful stories that only dragons know.

Answers to page 6

18 Focus of question: *deduction of character*
Award **1 mark** for answers which just state:

- No, Mr Pomeroy is not hard-hearted.

Award **2 marks** for answers which give supporting evidence, such as:

- No, Mr Pomeroy is not hard-hearted. We know this because he leaves the baby animals to grow up in his garden. Also, he does not let Snapping Jack disturb the baby animals.

19 Focus of question: *responding to whole story using textual evidence*
This question tests your child's insight and understanding of the story. Your child's answer must relate clearly to this story. Up to **3 marks** are possible for this question and you must decide how many marks to award your child's response.
Award **no marks** for very simple responses such as:

- I liked it.
- I did not like it.

Award **1 mark** for answers which are general and simple responses, such as:

- I liked the story because it was about baby animals.
- I liked the lawnmower being able to talk.

Award **2 marks** for more complex responses that extend or explain central events in the story, such as:

- The story was like a fantasy or fairy story because one of the characters was a dragon.
- I liked the story because Mr Pomeroy was kind to the creatures.

Award **3 marks** for answers that show insight and real understanding of characters and/or theme, such as:

- I liked the way the author used the story to show that a wild garden can be a refuge for birds and other animals.
- I liked the humour in the story. Snapping Jack was quite aggressive until he met the dragon!
- The story told us about the rewards of taking care of wildlife.

ENGLISH

Practice for

Key Stage 2

National tests

Ages 9–10

Reading Booklet

Country Matters

Reading
Booklet

Acknowledgements

John Foster for the use of 'Mowers' from
Things That Go, compiled by Tony Bradman ©
1989, John Foster (1989, Blackie).

Orion Children's Books Ltd for the use of
'Don't Cut the Lawn' by Margaret Mahy from
Downhill Crocodile Whizz by Margaret Mahy
© 1986, Margaret Mahy (1986, Dent; 1989,
Puffin).

**Let's Learn at Home: Test your child's English,
ages 9-10** © Scholastic Ltd, 1999

Reading
Booklet

Contents

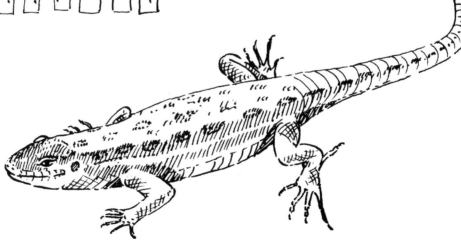

Don't Cut the Lawn!

by Margaret Mahy

Mr Pomeroy went to his seaside cottage for the holidays. The sea was right, the sand was right, the sun was right, the salt was right. But outside his cottage the lawn had grown into a terrible, tussocky tangle. Mr Pomeroy decided that he would have to cut it.

He got out his lawnmower, Snapping Jack.

'Now for some fun!' said Snapping Jack. 'Things have been very quiet lately. I've been wanting to get at that cheeky grass for weeks and weeks.'

Mr Pomeroy began pushing the lawnmower, and the grass flew up and out. However, he had gone only a few steps when out of the tangly, tussocky jungle flew a lark which cried,

'Don't cut the lawn, don't cut the lawn!
You will cut my little nestlings which have just been born.'

Mr Pomeroy went to investigate and there, sure enough, were four baby larks in a nest on the ground.

'No need to worry, Madam!' cried Mr Pomeroy to the anxious mother. 'We will go around your nest and cut the lawn further away.'

So they went around the nest and started cutting the lawn further away.

'Now for it!' said Snapping Jack, snapping away cheerfully. But at that moment out jumped a mother hare and cried,

'Don't cut the lawn, don't cut the lawn!
You will cut my little leveret which has just been
born.'

Mr Pomeroy went to investigate and there, sure enough, was a little brown leveret, safe in his own little tussocky form.

'We'll have to go further away to do our mowing,' Mr Pomeroy said to Snapping Jack. So they went further away and Mr Pomeroy said, 'Now we'll really begin cutting this lawn.'

'Right!' said Snapping Jack. 'We'll have no mercy on it.'

But they had only just begun to have no mercy on the lawn when a tabby cat leaped out of the tussocky tangle and mewed at them.

Don't cut the lawn, don't cut the lawn!
You will cut my little kittens which have just
been born.'

Mr Pomeroy went to investigate, and there, sure enough, were two stripy kittens in a little, golden tussocky, tangly hollow.

'This place is more like a zoo than a lawn,' grumbled Snapping Jack. 'We'll go further away this time, but you must promise to be hard-hearted or the lawn will get the better of us.'

'All right! If it happens again I'll be very hard-hearted,' promised Mr Pomeroy.

They began to cut where the lawn was longest, lankiest, tangliest and most terribly tough and tussocky.

'I'm not going to take any notice of any interruptions this time,' he said to himself firmly.

'We'll really get down to business,' said Snapping Jack, beginning to champ with satisfaction.

Then something moved in the long, lank, tussocky tangle.

Something slowly sat up and stared at them with jewelled eyes. It was a big mother dragon, as green as grass, as golden as a tussock. She looked at them and she hissed,

'Don't cut the lawn, don't cut the lawn!
You will cut my little dragon who has just been born.'

There, among the leathery scraps of the shell of the dragon's egg, was a tiny dragon, as golden and glittering as a bejewelled evening bag. It blew out a tiny flame at them, just like a cigarette lighter.

'Isn't he clever for one so young!' exclaimed his loving mother. 'Of course I can blow out a very big flame. I could burn all this lawn in one blast if I wanted to. I could easily scorch off your eyebrows.'

'Fire restrictions are on,' croaked the alarmed Mr Pomeroy.

'Oh, I'm afraid that wouldn't stop me,' said the dragon. 'Not if I were upset about anything. And if you mowed my baby I'd be very upset. I'd probably breathe fire hot enough to melt a lawnmower!'

'What do *you* think?' Mr Pomeroy asked Snapping Jack.

ENGLISH
Practice for
Key Stage 2
national tests

ages 9-10

Test and Answer Booklet

Country Matters

	MARKS
Page 3	
Page 4–5	
Page 6–7	
Page 8	
TOTAL	

	MARKS
Purpose and Organization	
Grammar – punctuation	
Grammar – style	
Spelling	
Handwriting	
TOTAL	

TOTAL SCORE	

First name

Last name

Reading test instructions

On pages 3–8 of this booklet there are different types of
questions for you to answer in different ways. The space for
your answer shows you what type of writing is needed.

- **short answers**

Some questions are followed by a short line. This shows that
you need only write a word or phrase in your answer.

- **several word answers**

Some questions are followed by a few lines.
This gives you space to write more words or a sentence or two.

- **longer answers**

Some questions are followed by a large box.
This shows that a longer, more detailed answer is needed to
explain your opinion. You can write in full sentences if you want
to.

- **multiple-choice answers**

For these answers you do not need to do any writing.
You need to choose the best word or group of words to fit the
passage or answer the question. Put a ring around your choice.

Marks
The number under each box in the margin tells you
the maximum number of marks for each question.

You will have 45 minutes for this test.
Refer to your reading booklet *Country Matters*
when you need to. You should work through the
questions in this booklet until you are asked to stop.

Let's learn at home
ENGLISH
Test and
Answer
Booklet

These questions are about the story
Don't Cut the Lawn!
Put a ring around the group of words that complete the
sentence.

Mr Pomeroy spent his holidays

1.

| in an hotel | by the sea | sailing a boat | playing cricket. |

1 mark

The lawn at his cottage was

2.

| lovely and smooth | brown and dry | like a field | very mossy. |

1 mark

Snapping Jack was the name of

3.

| Mr Pomeroy's cottage | the next door neighbour | Mr Pomeroy's dog | the lawnmower. |

1 mark

A lark had made a nest in

4.

| a tussock of grass | the lawnmower | a bush | the shed. |

1 mark

The little brown leveret belonged to

5.

| Snapping Jack | the lark | the mother hare | Mr Pomeroy. |

1 mark

Hidden in the longest grass was

6.

| the kitten | the baby dragon | the baby leveret | the lark. |

1 mark

1
2
3
4
5
6

TOTAL

PAGE 3

The lawn was left to grow because

7.

| Snapping Jack had broken down | it had started to rain | Snapping Jack was frightened of the mother dragon | Mr Pomeroy was tired. |

7

1 mark

Instead of cutting the lawn, Mr Pomeroy

8.

| fed the birds | went swimming | did some digging | mended the lawnmower. |

8

1 mark

Answer these questions in writing.

9. Why did the creatures choose to make nests in Mr Pomeroy's lawn?

_____

9

1 mark

10. Why didn't Mr Pomeroy get on with cutting the lawn once he had started?

_____

10

1 mark

11. What made the mother dragon proud of her baby?

_____

11

2 marks

12. The mother dragon can be very powerful. Write down **three** things she says that show she is powerful.

1. _____

2. _____

12

3 marks

3. _____

4

13. What was Snapping Jack thinking when he said, 'We don't want to upset a loving mother do we? Particularly one that breathes fire!'?

_____

_____

14. Choose **three** of the words below which best describe the mother dragon.

Copy these words on to the short lines.
Next to each one, explain why you have chosen it.

| dangerous | beautiful | frightening |

| protective | brave | fierce |

1. _____

2. _____

3. _____

15. How could a big creature like the dragon lie hidden in the grass? Find **two** reasons.

1. _____

2. _____

16. What do the characters all agree on at the end of the story?

_____

17. How did the baby dragon show his thanks to Mr Pomeroy for not cutting the grass?

_____

ENGLISH

Test and
Answer
Booklet

13

2 marks

14

3 marks

15

2 marks

16

1 mark

17

2 marks

TOTAL

PAGES 4-5

18. Is Mr Pomeroy hard-hearted? Find evidence from the story to back up your answer.

18

2 marks

_____

_____

_____

19. Write down what you think about the story _Don't Cut the Lawn!_ Explain your reasons for your ideas as fully as you can, referring to the story.

_____

_____

_____

_____

_____

_____

_____

_____

_____

_____

_____

19

3 marks

Test and Answer Booklet

These questions are about the poem *Mowers*.

1. Draw lines to match each phrase to the correct mower. One line has been done for you.

neat, straight lines

Jim's dad's mower

flinging grass cuttings everywhere

tears at the grass

Mrs Spencer's mower

hand-mower

electric mower

Grandad's mower

snorting like an angry bull

1a

2 marks

1b

2 marks

1c

2 marks

2. What do you think the lawn will look like when Jim's dad has finished mowing it?

_____

_____

2

1 mark

These questions are about the information pages *Wildlife in the Countryside*.

1. Complete the following table. Match up the statements to the animals. Mark the correct squares with a cross.

	lizard	hare	skylark
is brown in colour			
looks after its young			
makes a nest on the ground			
is a reptile			
lays eggs			
has live young			

1a

2 marks

1b

2 marks

1c

2 marks

TOTAL

PAGES 6-7

2. These three animals all have two things in common. What are they?

1. _____

2. _____

3. What makes it possible for these animals to nest on the ground without being easily detected?

_____

_____

4. Use the information about a wildlife garden to write a description of a wildlife garden for an encyclopaedia.

_____

_____

_____

_____

_____

_____

_____

_____

_____

_____

TOTAL Reading Score
pages 3, 5, 7 and 8

Writing test instructions

- On pages 10–11 and 14–15 of this booklet you will find a choice of four different things to write about. You must choose just **one**.

- On pages 12–13 and pages 16–17 there are planning sheets to help you organize your ideas before you begin to write.

> - The first **15 minutes** of the test are for you to think about what you are going to write. Use the planning pages to jot down your ideas during this time.

- Then write about your chosen title. Use lined paper.

> - You will have **45 minutes** to finish your writing.

Information writing

1. **Wildlife at school**

This year, Year 6 has created a wildlife garden in the school grounds. During the summer term, the children plan to make a pond.

> Write an article for the school newspaper explaining the work that has been done so far and what else needs to be done.

You may have experience of creating a real wildlife garden at home or at school, and could base your article on this knowledge.

Alternatively, make up information based on your general knowledge of wildlife and gardens.

You will need to inform your readers of some facts about the project, such as when it was started, where it is sited, results of work completed so far. You could also mention what plans there are for further development, and include some reasons why the school decided to develop a wildlife area.

In your article you could ask if any parents would be willing to help with digging out the pond or donating plants. You will need to persuade your readers that the project is worthwhile and that their help will be invaluable.

Remember to think about:

- who will read your article
- what the readers need to know
- why the wildlife garden was started
- what work has already been done and how it will develop
- what part of the work the children will do
- what outside help will be needed, and when it will be needed
- layout ideas (how the article will look).

2. A rabbit is rescued

You receive a letter from your friend who is on holiday. The letter tells you that your friend has found a young wild rabbit that has been deserted. Your friend asks you for advice on how to care for the rabbit.

> Write a letter to your friend, giving advice about what they must do to keep the young rabbit warm, fed and safe.

You should think about:
- how old the rabbit is
- where the rabbit lived naturally
- what food it is used to.

Your advice to your friend should include:
- where the rabbit should be kept
- what the living quarters should have for the rabbit's comfort
- what food it should have
- what should happen to it when it gets older.

11

Information writing planning sheet

Tick the title you have chosen.

1. Wildlife at school ⬡

2. A rabbit is rescued ⬡

Jot down some of your ideas. Plan your writing. Make some short notes. Your notes will **not** be marked.

Test and
Answer
Booklet

Use extra blank paper if you need to.

Story writing

3. Big becomes little

You and a friend are enjoying a picnic in a meadow full of tall grasses and wild flowers, when suddenly you shrink to being 5cm high!

Describe what you see and what minibeasts you meet. Write about the difficulties you have with being so very small.

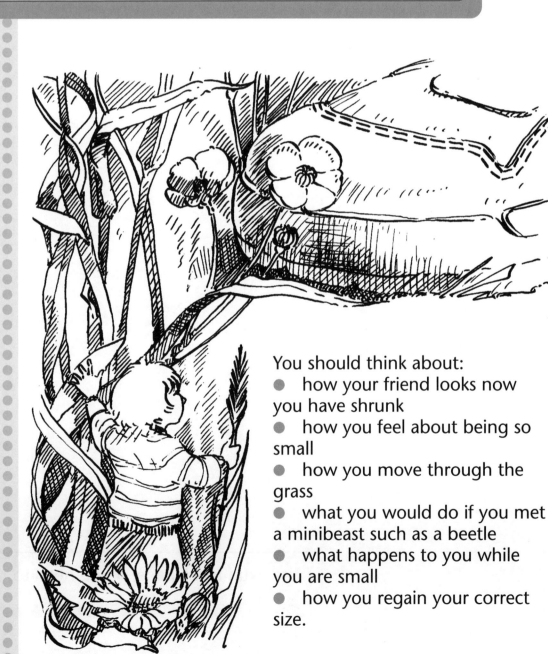

You should think about:

● how your friend looks now you have shrunk

● how you feel about being so small

● how you move through the grass

● what you would do if you met a minibeast such as a beetle

● what happens to you while you are small

● how you regain your correct size.

4. A garden mystery

Frankie's class was visiting a special garden with their teacher. Frankie lagged behind the others and noticed a small wooden door in the garden wall. The door was half open and through it, a tangled garden could just be seen. Frankie just had to explore…

Write a short story using this idea to help you. Plan your story using the planning sheet.

You will need to think about:
- who the characters are
- when and where the story is set
- how the story begins
- what adventure or event happens
- how the story will end.

ENGLISH

Test and
Answer
Booklet

Writing test

Story planning sheet

Tick the title you have chosen.

3. Big becomes little ☐   4. A garden mystery ☐

Remember to plan:
- setting
- characters
- how your story begins
- what happens
- how you will end your story.

Jot down some of your ideas. Plan your writing. Make some short notes. Your notes will **not** be marked.

16

Use extra blank paper if you need to.

Spelling and Handwriting test instructions

● Your parent or carer will read the first part of the story **Holidays** out loud to you.

> You will have **10 minutes** for the spelling test.

● Follow the story on pages 18 and 19 as it is read out. Do not write anything the first time you hear the story.

● Then your parent or carer will read out the story again. This time when you come to a space in the story, write the word you hear your parent or carer say.

● If you're not sure how to spell a word, have a go at it anyway.

● The short paragraph on page 20 finishes the story **Holidays**.

> You will have **5 minutes** for the handwriting test.

● Write it out as neatly as you can in your own handwriting.

● A mark will be given for your handwriting.

Holidays

At last the holidays had come! Amy and Tom had broken up from school a

week ago. Now they were _____ into the back of Auntie

Sita's old car on their way to a holiday cottage by the sea. As they weren't

sure what would be at the cottage, they had brought sleeping bags, some

candles, a big box of games and the portable television. Plus there was Ginger,

the pet hamster. Auntie Sita didn't think her car would survive the trip!

continued

Dad had _____ a _____ picnic lunch

for everyone, but they had eaten that hours ago. Tom was getting hungry

again. The journey seemed to be going on for ever. Amy was

_____ they were lost. Mum had the

_____ of the cottage in her bag, but the

_____ for the journey that Tom had worked out had been

left behind on the kitchen table.

    They _____ to stop at the next café and have a meal.

Mum _____ pizza for everyone, but Tom wanted

sausages and chips. Just as they were finishing, a _____

came into the café. Auntie Sita _____ him and asked if he

_____ where their cottage was. To their

_____, he knew exactly where it was

_____ he lived very _____.

    They _____ back into the car and

_____ their journey. By the time they arrived it was

_____ dark. It was a _____ to see the

cottage at last. Amy _____ they would be driving round

all _____!

Let's learn at home

ENGLISH

Test and
Answer
Booklet

Handwriting test

This short paragraph finishes the story. Write it out as neatly as you can in your own handwriting. A mark will be given for your handwriting.

The front door key was under a stone on the step. While Mum and Auntie Sita unpacked the car, Amy and Tom raced round to the back garden. They could smell the sea and hear the waves. Now the holidays could really begin. It was worth the long journey after all!

_____

_____

_____

_____

_____

_____

_____

_____

_____

Let's Learn at Home: Test your child's English, ages 9–10 © Scholastic Ltd, 1999

'Let's leave it until next week,' said Snapping Jack hurriedly. 'We don't want to upset a loving mother, do we? Particularly one that breathes fire!'

So the lawn was left alone and Mr Pomeroy sat on his verandah enjoying the sun, or swam in the sea enjoying the salt water, and day by day he watched the cottage lawn grow more tussocky and more tangly. Then, one day, out of the tussocks and tangles flew four baby larks which began learning how to soar and sing as larks do. And out of the tussocks and tangles came a little hare which frolicked and frisked as hares do. And out of the tussocks and tangles came two stripy kittens which pounced and bounced as kittens do. And *then* out of the tussocks and tangles came a little dragon with golden scales and eyes like stars, and it laid its shining head on Mr Pomeroy's knee and told him some of the wonderful stories that only dragons know. Even Snapping Jack listened with interest.

'Fancy that!' he was heard to remark. 'I'm glad I talked Mr Pomeroy out of mowing the lawn. Who'd ever believe a tussocky, tangly lawn could be home to so many creatures. There's more to a lawn than mere grass, you know!'

And Mr Pomeroy, the larks, the leveret, the kittens and the little dragon all agreed with him.

Mowers

Jim's dad has a motor mower.
He says it has a mind of its own.
It charges up and down their lawn
Snorting like an angry bull,
Flinging grass cuttings everywhere.

Mrs Spencer next door has an electric mower.
She bustles up and down her lawn,
Ironing it into neat, straight lines
Until there's not a blade of grass out of place.
Her lawn is as flat as a cricket pitch.

Grandad's got a hand-mower.
It rattles and clanks as he pushes it along.
It tears at the grass, chewing it up.
Grandad's lawn looks as if it's had a haircut
With a blunt pair of scissors.

John Foster

Wildlife in the countryside

A rich, grassland, wildlife meadow used to be a spin-off from traditional farming. It was the regular, methodical annual cycle of mowing and grazing which provided the ideal conditions for the wild flowers, butterflies, birds and animals that used to live in the countryside.

To create a wildlife area in your own garden, you will need to change the routine for mowing the grass. It is not simply a matter of neglecting the garden but of careful management!

The lawn will need to be left uncut until midsummer to give the grasses a chance to flower. You will have better success if your lawn is old and weedy and the soil beneath is poor. Leaving the mowing till midsummer gives the seeds of the spring flowers a chance to spread and germinate. Mowing the grass in July prevents the spring flowers being overtaken by the coarse grasses. It helps if the grass is trampled at the end of the summer, so ask a crowd of your friends along for a picnic on your wildlife area! The trampling helps the seeds to drop down through the grass and germinate. The grass should have two or three cuts at the end of the growing season in mid- to late September.

To get a good variety of wild flowers you will need to buy seeds and sprinkle them over the grass. You will need to check the type of soil you have. It might be acid or chalky, very wet or sandy and well-drained. You will find different types of soil provide a habitat for different groups of plants. The wild flowers in the hedgerows where you live will show you what would grow in your garden.

A wildlife garden provides the bottom layer of a food pyramid. The plants attract all kinds of insects including bees and butterflies. These in turn attract birds and small animals such as hedgehogs, moles and mice. These will attract bigger predators such as cats, weasels and owls. After two seasons of careful management, your wildlife garden will be a source of great interest and delight.

The common lizard
A common lizard lives on tufty heathland. The male grows to about 15cm in length. The female grows to about 18cm and has a bigger body. They are brownish in colour with orange undersides. They eat insects, caterpillars and spiders. They belong to the reptile family but unlike snakes, they can move their eyelids. The female lizard gives birth to six to twelve young on the open ground in the summer. The babies are left to fend for themselves.

The brown hare

The hare is similar to a rabbit to look at. It is a bigger animal than the rabbit with long back legs and long ears with black tips. Its coat is a tawny brown. It does not live in a burrow like a rabbit but nests in a hollow in the grass known as a 'form'. This is where the young leverets are born. They are born with their eyes open and have a short furry coat. The mother looks after her young until they are independent. Hares are vegetarians and eat tree bark, roots and plants.

The skylark

The skylark grows to about 18cm in length. It has striped brown feathers with white outer tail feathers. It lives in the open ground and makes its nest of dried grass on the surface of the ground. It mostly eats insects and seeds. It lays three to five speckled brown eggs in the spring, and feeds the chicks when they hatch out. The skylark is famous for its beautiful song.

ANSWERS TO READING TEST
Mowers by John Foster (poem)

Answers to page 7

1 Focus of question: *retrieval of information*
Award 2 marks for each pair of phrases correctly matched to each person's mower (up to 6 marks).

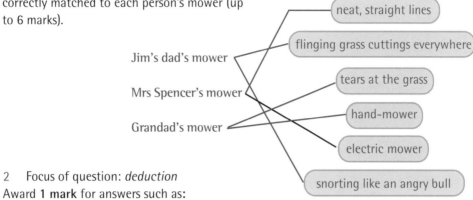

2 Focus of question: *deduction*
Award **1 mark** for answers such as:
● The lawn will be covered with grass cuttings.
● There may be parts of the lawn that didn't get properly cut.
● There won't be any lines or stripes left on the grass by the mower.

ANSWERS TO READING TEST
Wildlife in the Countryside (information)

Answers to pages 7–8

1 Focus of question: *retrieval of information; deduction*
Award **2 marks** for each animal correctly matched with **its four** attributes (up to **6 marks**):

	lizard	hare	skylark
is brown in colour	X	X	X
looks after its young		X	X
makes a nest on the ground	X	X	X
is a reptile	X		
lays eggs			X
has live young	X	X	

2 Focus of question: *identification of similarities*

Award **1 mark** for answers along the following lines:
● They all have brown colouring.
● They all make their nests on the surface of the ground.

3 Focus of question: *deduction*
Award **1 mark** for answers along the following lines:
● Their colouring helps them to hide/blend into the background.
● Their colouring acts as a camouflage.
● Their colouring makes them difficult to see against the earth and grass.

4 Focus of question: *retrieve and recast information*
The question asks for a description for an encyclopaedia, so children should take care to include only facts, not opinions.

Parent's
Booklet

Award **1 mark** for answers that provide a very simple description with minor facts about a wildlife garden, such as:

- The grass is only cut once or twice a year.
- It has wild flowers and plants.
- The flowers attract birds and animals.

Award **2 marks** for answers that identify more than one key characteristic, such as:

- The grass is left uncut. Bees and butterflies visit.
- Lots of wild grasses grow. Wild animals such as hares may live there.

Award **4 marks** for more complex answers that identify several features and give evidence of reworking the reading passage, such as:

- The grass is left uncut to allow the grasses to flower.
- The lawn needs trampling to allow the seeds to drop through the grass and germinate.

- It takes about a year to make a wildlife garden. It makes a good habitat for flowers, insects and wild animals and birds such as hares, lizards and skylarks.

Award **5 marks** for answers that show thinking about encyclopaedia layout (for example, use of headings) and include lots of relevant points to give a full description, such as:

A Wildlife Garden

A wildlife garden needs careful management of mowing and trampling. The soil should be poor and the grass cutting properly managed to encourage wild flowers to germinate. Wild flowers that grow locally grow best in the garden. The plants that grow in a wildlife garden attract insects and butterflies which attract birds and small animals and these attract larger predators.

ANSWERS TO WRITING TEST

In National Tests, the writing test is assessed under two broad categories:

- **Purpose and Organization** – this refers to the **content** of your child's writing.
- **Grammar** (subdivided into **punctuation** and **style**) – this refers to **how** your child writes his or her answer.

Parent's tip

Your child's **planning notes** are useful for you to check that he or she has made good use of the planning time. It is important that your child uses the planning time and notes in the test. They will help your child to have a clear idea of what he or she is going to write before starting the answers.

Marks scheme

35 marks are available for this test. The marks are subdivided according to the above categories as follows:

Purpose and Organization	21 marks
Grammar – punctuation	7 marks
Grammar – style	7 marks
Total	**35 marks**

To mark your child's writing you need to assess it, using the following tables.

Read the descriptions for each of the categories given above. For each piece of writing, levels of achievement are described for Levels 2, 3, 4 and 5. For each level the appropriate mark is given. It is up to you to decide which description best fits your child's writing, and award a mark accordingly. Enter the mark for each separate category on the front cover of the Test and Answer Booklet.

8

Purpose and Organization

LEVEL 2 — 9 MARKS

Level 2 information writing usually has:
- clear meaning
- a series of brief statements which may not be connected
- appropriate and interesting vocabulary.

Level 2 information writing may have:
- elements of text organization, eg opening and closing statements
- awareness of reading audience by reference.

Level 2 story writing usually has:
- basic elements of story structure: a clear opening, a sequence of events and an ending
- two or more events (real or imagined)
- chronological sequence
- one or more named characters.

Level 2 story writing may have:
- simple details in descriptions of events and characters
- simple story language such as 'Once upon a time...'

LEVEL 3 — 12 MARKS

Level 3 information writing usually has:
- appropriate basic structures to convey the information, such as an opening statement and a series of relevant points made in a logical sequence
- general coverage of the topic
- vocabulary chosen for variety and interest
- details that will clarify the information or create added interest.

Level 3 information writing may have:
- patchy coverage of the topic with some aspects having more weight than others
- the writer's opinions of approval or disapproval.

Level 3 story writing usually has:
- main features of story structure – a beginning, a middle and an appropriate but simple ending
- events connected to one another
- events in a chronological sequence
- simple description of story setting
- a sense of what characters think and feel
- simple but interesting details
- an attempt to interest the reader.

LEVEL 4 — 18 MARKS

Level 4 information writing usually has:
- appropriate conventions, such as a suitable introduction, a series of correctly sequenced points and a concluding phrase or sentence
- layout that is generally appropriate
- evidence that the writer has intended to inform the reader by presenting the information clearly
- points intended to persuade the reader
- sustained and logically developed ideas
- overall coherence and adequate coverage of a range of relevant aspects
- more adventurous choice of vocabulary and words used for effect.

Level 4 story writing usually has:
- clear elements of story – a suitable beginning, a middle and a convincing ending
- events that follow logically from one to another
- a sense of what characters think and feel
- interaction between different characters, shown by what they say or do
- good pace
- an attempt to engage the reader's attention.

LEVEL 5 — 21 MARKS

Level 5 information writing usually has:
- competent use of relevant conventions, including layout
- an attempt to engage the reader's attention, with
  - an introduction that sets the writing in context and establishes its purpose
  - a series of points that are linked to the purpose of the piece
  - a conclusion that draws the whole piece to a close
- good structure and development
- convincing points
- adequate coverage of the different key aspects of the topic
- clear organization using paragraphs or other layout devices such as headings or diagrams
- imaginatively chosen vocabulary, accurately used.

Level 5 story writing usually has:
- a strong story structure
- conformity to a story type such as realistic narrative, adventure, fable and so on
- interwoven elements of description, action and dialogue
- an attempt to catch and sustain the reader's interest by using narrative techniques such as a dramatic beginning
- good pace and organization.

Level 5 story writing may have:
- evidence that the writer is in control, such as comments on characters' actions, feelings and thoughts
- paragraphs to show changes of scene, new events or to introduce new characters
- flashbacks to other times or places, a subplot or a twist.

ANSWERS TO WRITING TEST

Grammar – punctuation

Grammar – style

LEVEL 2

2 MARKS

Level 2 writing has:
- correct use of capital letters and full stops in at least two places.

2 MARKS

Level 2 writing has:
- ideas linked by 'and', 'then', 'so', 'but'
- fairly simple vocabulary such as 'made', 'good', 'see'.

LEVEL 3

4 MARKS

Level 3 writing has:
- accurate use of capital letters, full stops and, where appropriate, question marks in at least half of the sentences
- where appropriate, inverted commas to show direct speech.

4 MARKS

Level 3 writing usually has:
- linking words to join ideas or events ('but', 'and'), to make connections in time ('when', 'also') or to explain ('so', 'because')
- descriptive phrases with simple adverbs such as 'quietly' and adjectives such as 'small', 'cold'
- subjects and verbs within sentences that usually agree
- vocabulary appropriate to the intended readership.

LEVEL 4

5 MARKS

Level 4 writing has:
- accurate use of full stops, question marks and capital letters in most of the sentences
- correct use of punctuation within some sentences, such as commas to separate short phrases, clauses or listed items
- use of inverted commas, where appropriate, to begin and end direct speech.

5 MARKS

Level 4 writing usually has:
- a mixture of simple and complex sentences
- phrases to clarify meaning
- different types of sentence connectives ('if', 'when', 'although', 'however') to order ideas and give emphasis
- attempts at impersonal constructions where appropriate
- well-chosen words or phrases to give interest and precision
- more adventurous vocabulary
- consistent use of tenses and pronouns.

LEVEL 5

7 MARKS

Level 5 writing has:
- accurate use of full stops, question marks and capital letters in almost all sentences
- commas and speech marks to introduce and conclude direct speech
- capital letters for proper nouns
- apostrophes to show possession or letters missed out
- a range of appropriate punctuation marks such as brackets, dashes, bullet points and exclamation marks to enhance text layout, vary pace and add colour to descriptions.

7 MARKS

Level 5 writing usually has:
- a variety of simple and complex sentences that give shape, interest and pace to the writing
- precise language, with technical and specific vocabulary where appropriate
- imaginative choice of vocabulary where appropriate to heighten effect
- a more impersonal style or use of the passive tense to alter the focus of attention and convey instructions
- language that is chosen with appropriate awareness of audience and purpose
  – in information writing, there is an appropriate level of formality
  – in story writing there is standard English, dialect or colloquialisms, and imagery for effect.

ANSWERS TO SPELLING AND HANDWRITING TEST

A total of **15 marks** are available for this test, split up as follows:

Spelling	10 marks
Handwriting	5 marks
Total	**15 marks**

Ask your child to turn to the Spelling and Handwriting test on page 18 of the Test and Answer Booklet. These two tests are always done together. Read through the instructions with your child and make sure he or she understands them.

Parent's tip

The first time you read the spelling test, do so without stopping. The second time you read it, pause when you read each word printed in **bold**, so that your child has time to write the spellings in the spaces on test pages 18 and 19.

The spelling passage

Holidays

At last the holidays had come! Amy and Tom had broken up from school a week ago. Now they were **jammed** into the back of Auntie Sita's old car on their way to a holiday cottage by the sea. As they weren't sure what would be at the cottage, they had brought sleeping bags, some candles, a big box of games and the portable television. Plus there was Ginger, the pet hamster. Auntie Sita didn't think her car would survive the trip!

Dad had **packed** a **delicious** picnic lunch for everyone, but they had eaten that hours ago. Tom was getting hungry again. The journey seemed to be going on for ever. Amy was **sure** they were lost. Mum had the **address** of the cottage in her bag, but the **directions** for the journey that Tom had worked out had been left behind on the kitchen table.

They **decided** to stop at the next café and have a meal. Mum **ordered** pizza for everyone, but Tom wanted sausages and chips. Just as they were finishing, a **policeman** came into the café. Auntie Sita **approached** him and asked if he **knew** where their cottage was. To their **surprise**, he knew exactly where it was **because** he lived very **near**.

They **climbed** back into the car and **continued** their journey. By the time they arrived it was **nearly** dark. It was a **relief** to see the cottage at last. Amy **thought** they would be driving round all **night**!

Enter your child's Spelling test mark on page 19 of
the Test and Answer Booklet.

Marks	
number of correct words	Spelling test mark
1–2	1
3–4	2
5–6	3
7–8	4
9–10	5
11–12	6
13–14	7
15–16	8
17–18	9
19–20	10

ANSWERS TO HANDWRITING TEST

Ask your child to turn to page 20 of the
Test and Answer Booklet. Remind him or
her of the test instructions on page 18.
You need to assess your child's
handwriting using the descriptions below,
then award it the appropriate mark. Enter
your child's Handwriting test mark on
page 20 of the Test and Answer Booklet.
Remember that you are looking for the
description that best fits your child's
handwriting, not an exact match.

LEVEL 2

2 MARKS

Letters not joined, but legible. Some inconsistencies
of letter shape and word spacing.

LEVEL 3

3 MARKS

Letters partially joined. Clear and legible,
with consistent spacing between words.
Letters are uniform in size.

LEVEL 4

4 MARKS

Letters are joined. Appearance is more fluent and
legible. Correct formation of letters and consistent
spacing between words. Letters are uniform in size.

LEVEL 5

5 MARKS

Clear, legible and joined handwriting.
Expresses confidence and stylistic
maturity.